What Has Spots ?

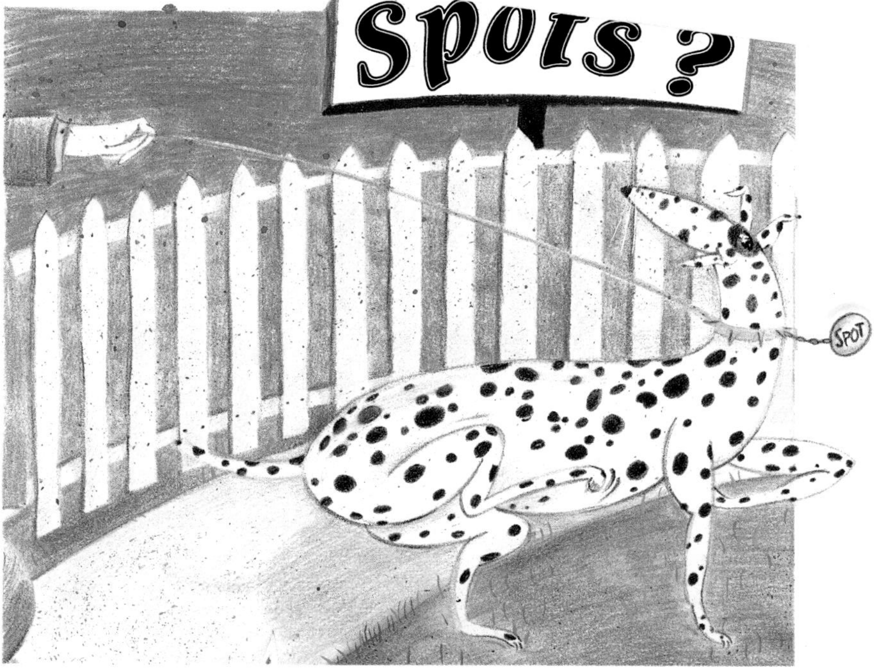

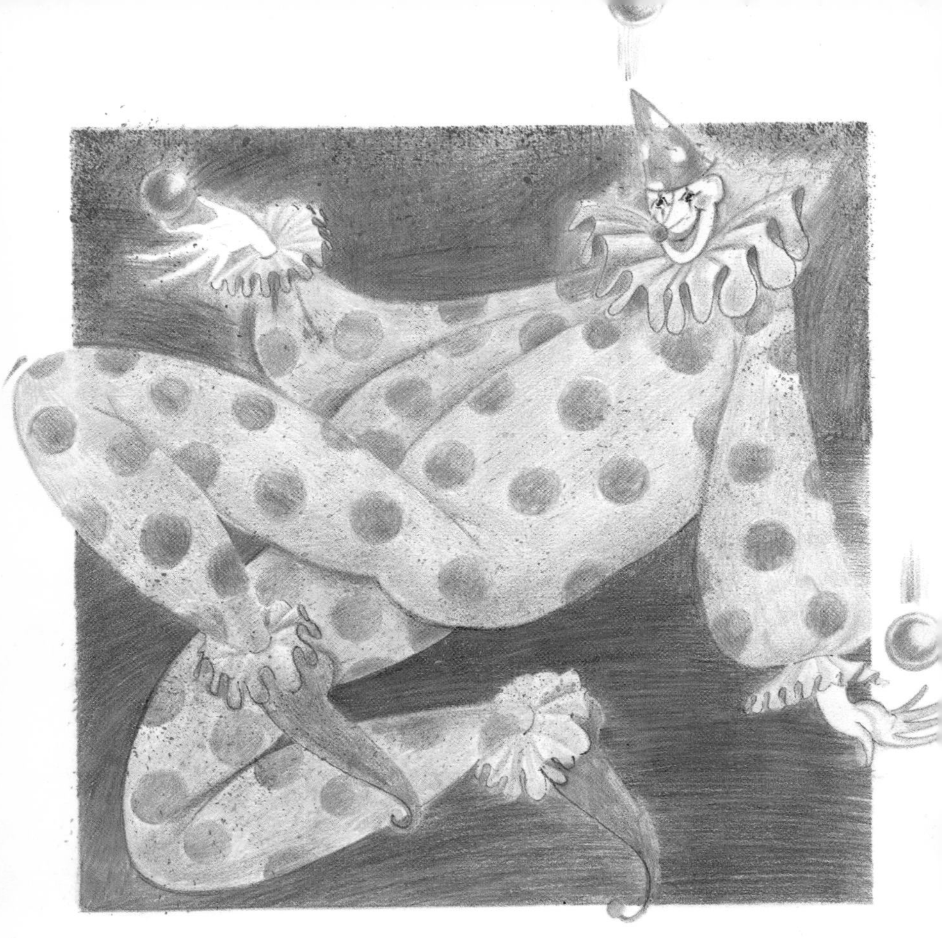

This clown has spots.

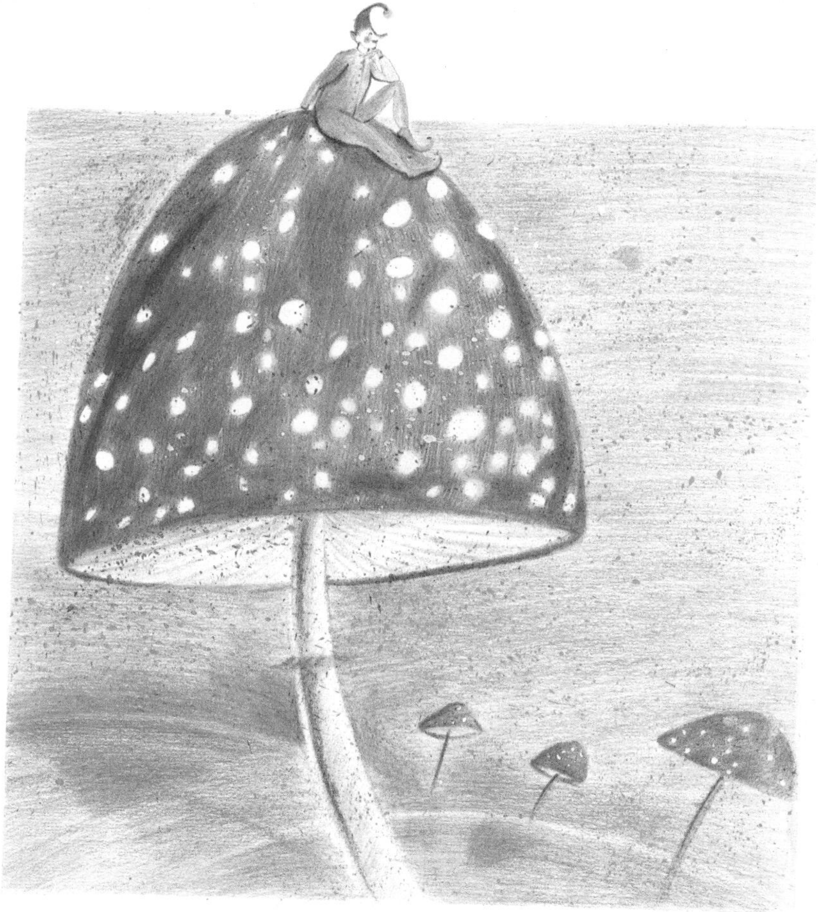

This toadstool has spots.

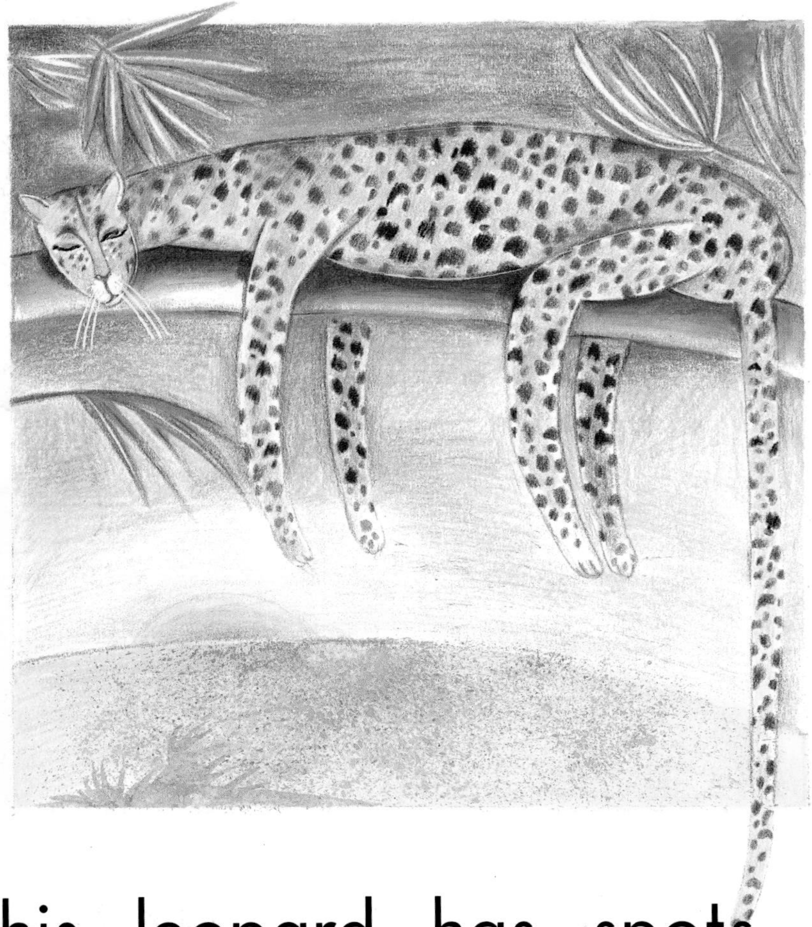

This leopard has spots.

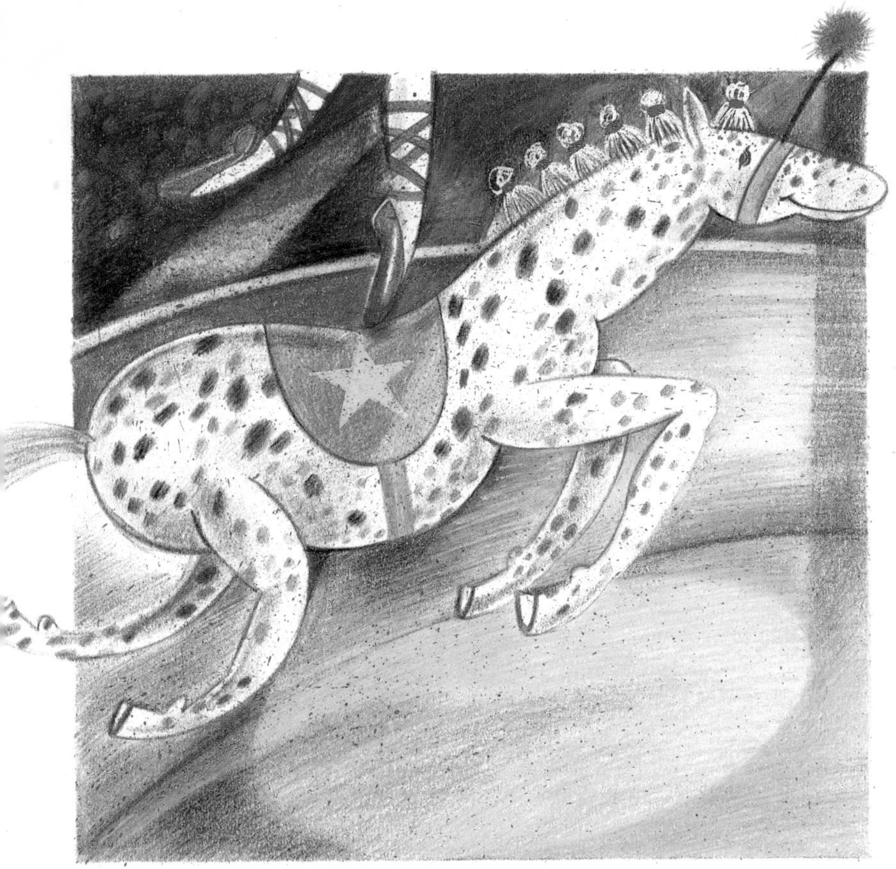

This horse has spots.

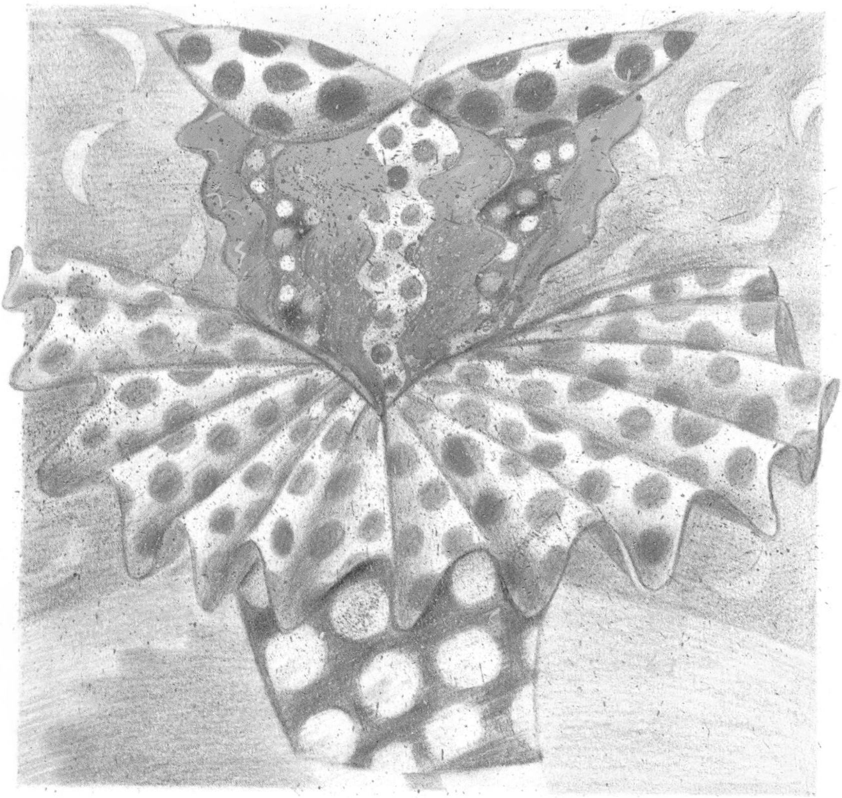

This dress has spots.

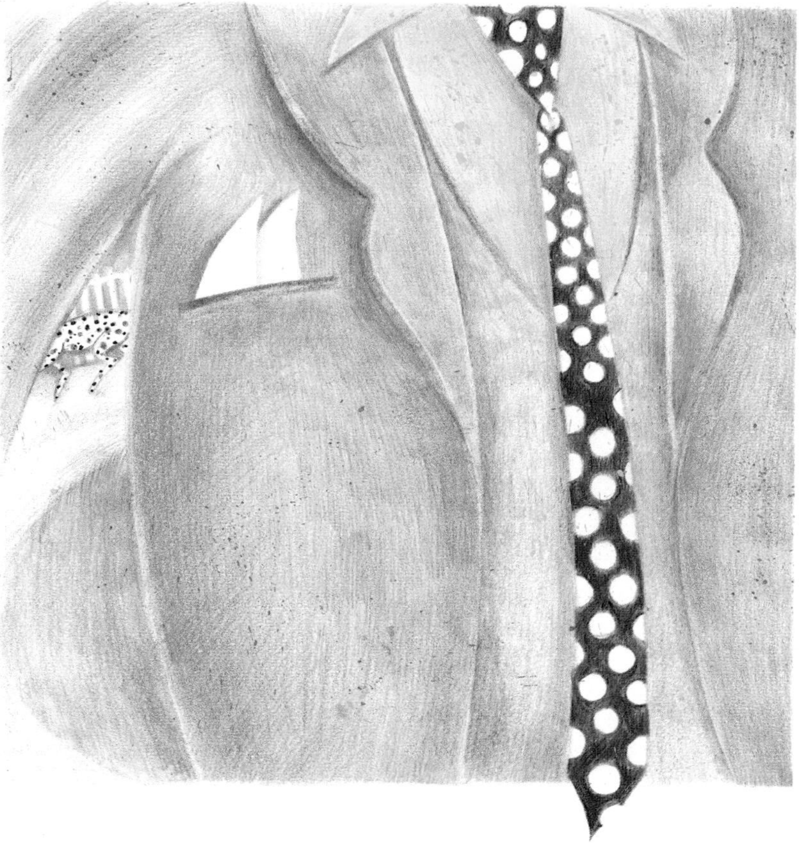

This tie has spots.

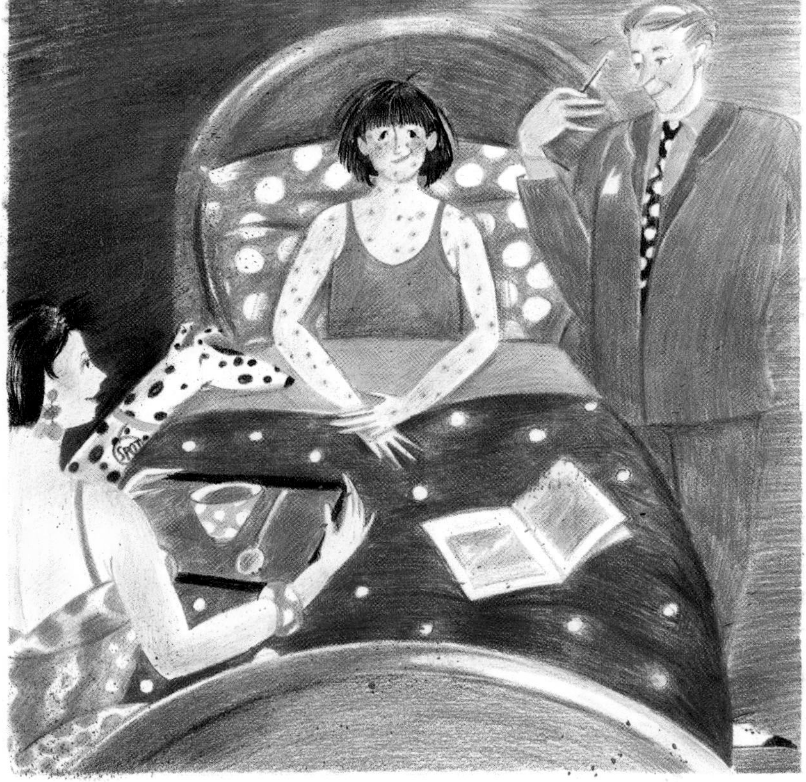

And this girl has spots.